To Fredrick Eaton.

d. d.

[illegible]

In nativitate
Sancti Johannis
Baptistae.

Stowe. March 11th. MVIM.

Drawings of Stowe by John Claude Nattes in the Buckinghamshire County Museum

C. N. Gowing and G. B. Clarke

Buckinghamshire County Museum and Stowe School

ISBN 0 86059 282 0

Introduction

Nattes's views of Stowe are first mentioned at the sale of the library of Stowe House, which took place in January 1849, soon after the bankruptcy of the Second Duke of Buckingham and Chandos. The sale was conducted by S. Leigh, Sotheby and Co., and Lot 5197 of their catalogue was described as 'Stowe (Views of) and taken in 1805-6-7-9, consisting of 110 original drawings, in crayon, bistre, &c. by J. C. Nattes, 2 vol. *russia* . . . oblong folio, *n.d.*' Though this description is not entirely accurate—there are 105 drawings, not 110, and none of them was done in 1806—the two albums of the present collection must be the volumes referred to. It is also recorded that they were bought by a well-known bookseller named J. T. Payne, who paid £30 for them; and since the two volumes later appear in the catalogue of Sir Thomas Phillipps, Bt. (under the entry MS 13748) as having been bought from the Duke of Buckingham, it is probable that Payne was buying them on commission for Sir Thomas. The drawings returned to the sale-room on 29th June, 1926, as Lot 101 in the Sotheby Parke Bernet & Co.'s sale of the Phillipps Collection, when they were bought for £56 by Mr. Rimell, a London bookseller. Thereafter their history is obscure. They were seen by I. A. Williams, who referred to them briefly in *Early English Watercolours* (1952), and for a time they must have been in the possession of Mr. H. Stonor, whose name appears on the first page with a date—23rd November, 1941. The only certain fact is that in the summer of 1980, after one or more changes of ownership, they came into the hands of Mr. Ben Weinreb, of Architectural Books Ltd., 93 Great Russell Street, who offered them for sale.

It was first suggested that Stowe School, as heir to Stowe House, might wish to regain the two albums, and that the school library might be an appropriate home for these unique views of Stowe's buildings and landscape. The Governors of the School took up the idea with interest, but the price asked (£40,000) was beyond the School's resources. It was then proposed that an attempt should be made to acquire the drawings for the Buckinghamshire County Museum at Aylesbury, a course of action which was pursued with the active support of Stowe's Governors. Happily this scheme met with success. The limited funds available to the County Museum were supplemented by two substantial grants from the National Heritage Fund and the Victoria and Albert Museum, and the balance of the purchase price was made up by three generous personal gifts from former members of Stowe School. So, in the late autumn of 1980, Nattes's views of Stowe arrived at the County Museum.

A year later, while the drawings were being examined by a conservation expert, the School asked the Museum for permission to reproduce some of them in 1983, to mark the sixtieth anniversary of the School's foundation. The Museum welcomed the idea, asking in turn that it should become partner in the enterprise and suggesting that publication should take the form of a full catalogue of the drawings, reproducing as many of them as possible. Agreement was quickly reached, and the present volume, jointly published by the County Museum and Stowe School, is the result of their partnership.

There are one hundred and five drawings in the collection. All are executed on English-made paper, sixty-seven on laid and thirty-eight on wove paper, and the presence of punch holes along the edges of some drawings shows that the paper was secured to a drawing-frame while they were being executed. The principal medium is wash, with fifty-eight examples in shades of grey and a further eighteen drawings with a combination of sepia and grey washes. Most of these washes are done over pencil; in many of them brush in black ink is also used, and in a number pen and black ink. Of the other drawings black chalk is used in twenty-seven, and two are in pencil. It is noticeable that all the drawings of 1807 involve the use of grey washes, and that none of them uses a sepia wash or black chalk. When the drawings were finished, they were mounted with starch paste on a crude rag paper, usually laid but sometimes wove, and it was on this mount that the inscription was written. At a later date the drawings were placed on a second, larger mounting, using the same starch paste as adhesive, and were interleaved; then they were bound into two leather volumes with a printed title page.

This description of the methods of mounting the drawings is based on information kindly provided by Miss Jane McAusland, who undertook the examination and conservation of the drawings. She found their general condition very good, though a few were badly stained. To preserve them better, the drawings have now been removed from the albums and lifted aqueously from their mountings. The immediate backing mount, which bears the inscription, has been hinged to the drawing, and both have been re-mounted together in conservation mountings.

The catalogue of the drawings lists them in the same order as they were mounted in the two albums, in which the arrangement followed approximately the sequence set out on the printed title page added to each album. This reads: *VIEWS OF STOWE, &c. taken in the Years 1805, 1806, and 1807, by C. Nattes. ARRANGEMENT: Buckingham—The Great Avenue to the Arch—The Entrance to the Gardens—The Outside Tour of the W. Side of the Gardens—The Outside Tour of the E. Side of the Gardens—The Inside Tour of the W. Side of the Gardens—The Inside Tour of the E. Side of the Gardens—Views in the Park—The House. LONDON: Printed by B. R. Howlett, 49, Brewer Street, Golden Square.* Several points arise from this title page. In the first place it seems that the volumes must have been bound up some years after the drawings were completed, since the printer B. R. Howlett is registered as being at 49 Brewer Street only between 1811 and 1815. Secondly, '1806' must be an error for '1809'. There are clear dates on ninety-seven of the one hundred and five drawings (67 are of 1805, 10 of 1807 and 20 of 1809), and it is possible to assign all but one of the remainder to a particular year with reasonable confidence, after considering their subject, technique and watermark: three (Nos. 42, 78 and 90) seem to be of 1805, two (Nos. 37 and 99) of 1807, and two (Nos. 102 and 103) of 1809. The drawing not yet considered (No. 94, of the Marble Saloon) raises a further point, for it is not by Nattes but an amateur hand. The final section listed on the title page is *The House,* the natural climax to the sequence of Stowe views. But though there are views taken inside the north and south porticoes, and views of the north colonnades and of the greenhouses, and views of the basement passages and the service courts, no picture by Nattes of the Entrance Front or the Garden Front of the House is included. The great set pieces are missing. Instead there is a single, rather pallid drawing of the Marble Saloon by an unknown amateur.

In one sense, of course, the omission is of little consequence. We know well enough what the main house looked like in Nattes's time, for we have Medland's views of a decade earlier and Buckler's of a decade later, and in any case the north and south fronts of the House survive, hardly altered, to this day. It is much more valuable to have secret corners of Stowe, which no-one else records, revealed through Nattes's loving and perceptive eyes: the little path which meanders along the shore of the Octagon towards a long-vanished bridge, the wooden seat for tired walkers curving round a great oak in the Elysian Fields, or the stable court with its two levels and an astonishing luxuriance of foliage. It is inconceivable that Nattes did not include the two fronts of the house among his views, but they would have been the easiest to dispose of, and we can only assume that they were sold or given away before the drawings were placed in their final order.

This order, however, is not the only arrangement that was proposed. Numbers which bear no relation to it can be seen pencilled on a dozen of the early drawings. Indeed, the drawings of 1805 make up a comprehensive and attractive collection on their own, and it seems that during the two later years Nattes was doing little more than filling in the gaps. In 1807 he added the Fane of Pastoral Poetry and the basement of the house; and in 1809, the temples of Bacchus and Concord, four views of the approach from Buckingham and three of the service courts. But there is not much else of originality or interest from either year, most of the views being inferior versions of scenes he had drawn before. Everything points to 1805 as the decisive year in which he made some arrangement with Lord Buckingham to do a series of drawings at Stowe, with a view to their being engraved and published; and his draft frontispiece, whi survives, is reproduced on the opposite page. Such a scheme would have suited the ambitions of both men.

George, Marquess of Buckingham, owner of Stowe since 1779 and proud as a peacock, set out to be one of the great patrons of his age. He was an energetic builder and planter, like his two predecessors at Stowe, Viscount Cobham and Earl Temple, though the range and complexity of their work left him scope for only relatively minor schemes. So he turned to collecting books and manuscripts, paintings and prints, and became a considerable connoisseur. Two great series of topographical engravings of Stowe had previously been published, Rigaud's set in the 1730s during Lord Cobham's reign, and the Chatelain-Bickham set in the 1750s during Lord Temple's. But though an improved edition of the guide book had come out in 1797, with new illustrations based on drawings by Medland, no new set of engravings had appeared for fifty years. Stowe's landscape was now reaching mature perfection, and Nattes might be the artist destined to record it, thereby adorning the reign of Lord Buckingham.

It would equally have suited John Claude Nattes. In 1805 he was about forty and at the height of his reputation. He had just completed a series of engraved views of Scotland *(Scotia Depicta)* and another of Bath and Bristol; the first instalment of a series on *Versailles, Paris and Saint Denis* had recently been issued, and a series on Ireland *(Hibernia Depicta)* was projected. A year earlier he had been a founder member of the 'Old' Society of Painters in Water-Colours. So a set of Stowe engravings offered an intelligent step forward in his career: he would gain the patronage of one of the aristocratic princes of England, and at the same time extend the range of his topographical views to include great houses and their landscapes.

In the event, nothing came of it. Two years later, in 1807, Nattes was accused of exhibiting other artists' work in his own name and expelled from the Water-Colour Society. However, he returned to Stowe in the same year, and again in 1809, perhaps to be resident drawing-master there at the invitation of Lady Buckingham, herself an enthusiastic and talented artist. But, for reasons unknown, none of his views of Stowe was published. Eventually all that were left seem to have been put together in two albums and handed over to the family. They are not recorded in the manuscript library catalogue of 1812, but they were probably there by 1815, when it appears that the title page of the albums had been printed by Mr. Howlett. An occasion which would fit all the dates is 1813, when the Marquess of Buckingham died. After a decent interval Nattes could well have thought it worth offering the drawings to his successor, the Second Marquess.

On one of the drawings (No. 29) the actual day of the month is inscribed as well as the year, and the date indicates that Nattes was working at Stowe during the five-day visit of the Prince of Wales in August 1805. Other visitors were there too, including Betsy Fremantle with her young son Tom and her sister Harriet Wynne, who had come over from nearby Swanbourne. Fortunately the Wynne sisters were habitual diarists. Betsy's comments seem a little prim. 'The Prince was in high glee,' she wrote, '& rather more merry than a Prince ought to be.' But her younger, unmarried sister Harriet was less inhibited. She struck up a close friendship with Lady Mary, the lively daughter of Lord and Lady Buckingham, and in her diary entry for Wednesday, August 21st, we get a brief glimpse of Nattes at Stowe. 'At twelve we met at the Temple of Venus to see Mr. Nattes draw he is very good Artist and takes views enormously well. Lady Mary took me and we were very merry, for sometime.' The next day they joined him again. 'At twelve we went to draw with Mr. Nattes. I took a sketch passablement bien . . . Lady Mary and I were the whole morning with Nattes and we sung to him whilst he drew.' It seems that Nattes was working in the South Portico of the house that morning, for in the muniment room at Swanbourne there is a drawing almost identical with one of Nattes's (No. 96, Plate 47), right down to the last flower pot, but taken from a yard or so to the left. The Swanbourne version has no figures in it, but Nattes has added a young woman sitting on the seat with a child at her knee, who must be Betsy and young Tom. In a companion drawing looking the other way from the portico (No. 95) Nattes has added the figures of two slim girls in their early twenties. It was no doubt a gallant compliment to Lady Mary and Harriet, who sang the morning away for him while he sat there drawing. And the same young friends probably appear in another drawing (No. 91, Plate 45) looking over his shoulder to see what his latest view is like.

Statue of George I *Cat. No. 90*

The critics have not been kind to Nattes. Most of them have seized on his expulsion from the Water-Colour Society and have dismissed him in a few disparaging sentences. I. A. Williams goes further, attacking his 'coarse boldness of touch which is characteristic but not often attractive', a judgement which many will regard as unduly harsh after looking through the drawings reproduced here. Admittedly his work is uneven, but he is a topographical artist of great accomplishment, and the animated groups of figures giving scale to his scenes are a continual source of delight. Naturally, the drawings will have a special appeal for anyone who has spent part of his life at Stowe. Not all the scenes will be familiar, for many things have changed since 1805, but much remains that is nostalgic and evocative.

The drawings also have a particular interest for two groups of specialists. For the local historian they provide a surprising amount of new evidence, quite apart from the three pictures showing the temporary structures put up to fête the Prince of Wales. New buildings at Stowe can usually be dated from the guide books, which were brought up to date and re-issued every two or three years. But it happens that no new edition came out after 1797 for more than fifteen years. So Nattes conveniently helps to fill the gap, and his views are the first evidence that the Egyptian Hall and the Seasons' Fountain were both completed by 1805, and the Buckingham Lodges by 1809. Several of his views of the buildings, and many of the landscape gardens, are also unique. There are no other illustrations of Cook's Monument surmounted by its globe, nor of the interior of the Temple of Bacchus; and the appearance of the Keeper's Lodge in the park, before it was remodelled as the Bourbon Tower, is otherwise known only from a scrappy quarter-page engraving. However, Nattes was not infallible. He must have misunderstood the details of his rough sketch when he came to work up the drawing of the Egyptian Hall (No. 98, Plate 48), for 'the Egyptian emblems of the Egg and the Serpent' appear as the winged heads of traditional Renaissance putti.

Even more important is the information which the drawings offer to the landscape designer and conservationist. For here is Stowe pictured in its prime, in those magic decades between immaturity and decline. For nearly a century the lay-out had been continuously altered, the same areas being worked over again and again by several designers in turn. But by 1800 the lay-out and the garden buildings were complete, and the trees planted by Bridgeman and Kent in the 1720s and 1730s were reaching their full size. The aim of Stowe's modern restorers has been to repair the buildings and reconstruct the landscape gardens, so far as that is possible, to what they were at this classic moment. And now, as if to confirm their decision, a hundred views of Stowe taken a year or two after 1800 have been laid before them. They will not place too much reliance on Nattes when choosing the species of trees to plant, for his trees belong to the picturesque convention of the Romantic era, but their size, the density of their planting and their relationship to buildings, to water, and to grass, are very revealing. No doubt Nattes idealised his views, omitting imperfections on the ground. But the essence of English gardening is the idealisation of Nature, and it is the privilege of an artist to realise, at the stroke of his brush, the vision which a gardener labours for a lifetime to achieve.

Key to the Plan

1. Wolfe's Obelisk
2. Grecian Valley
3. Temple of Concord and Victory
4. Equestrian Statue of George I
5. Lord Cobham's Pillar
6. Queen's Temple
7. Keeper's Lodge
8. House
9. Orangery
10. Temple of Bacchus
11. Grotto
12. Alder River
13. Seasons' Fountain
14. Gothic Temple
15. Captain Cook's Monument
16. Grenville Column
17. Church
18. Temple of Ancient Virtue
19. Elysian Fields
20. Temple of British Worthies
21. Rotunda
22. Doric Arch
23. Palladian Bridge
24. Site of Wooden Bridge
25. Congreve's Monument
26. Pebble Alcove
27. Octagon Lake
28. Cascade
29. Eleven-Acre Lake
30. Queen Caroline's Monument
31. Boycott Pavilion
32. Temple of Venus
33. Lake Pavilions
34. Bell Gate
35. Temple of Friendship
36. Corinthian Arch

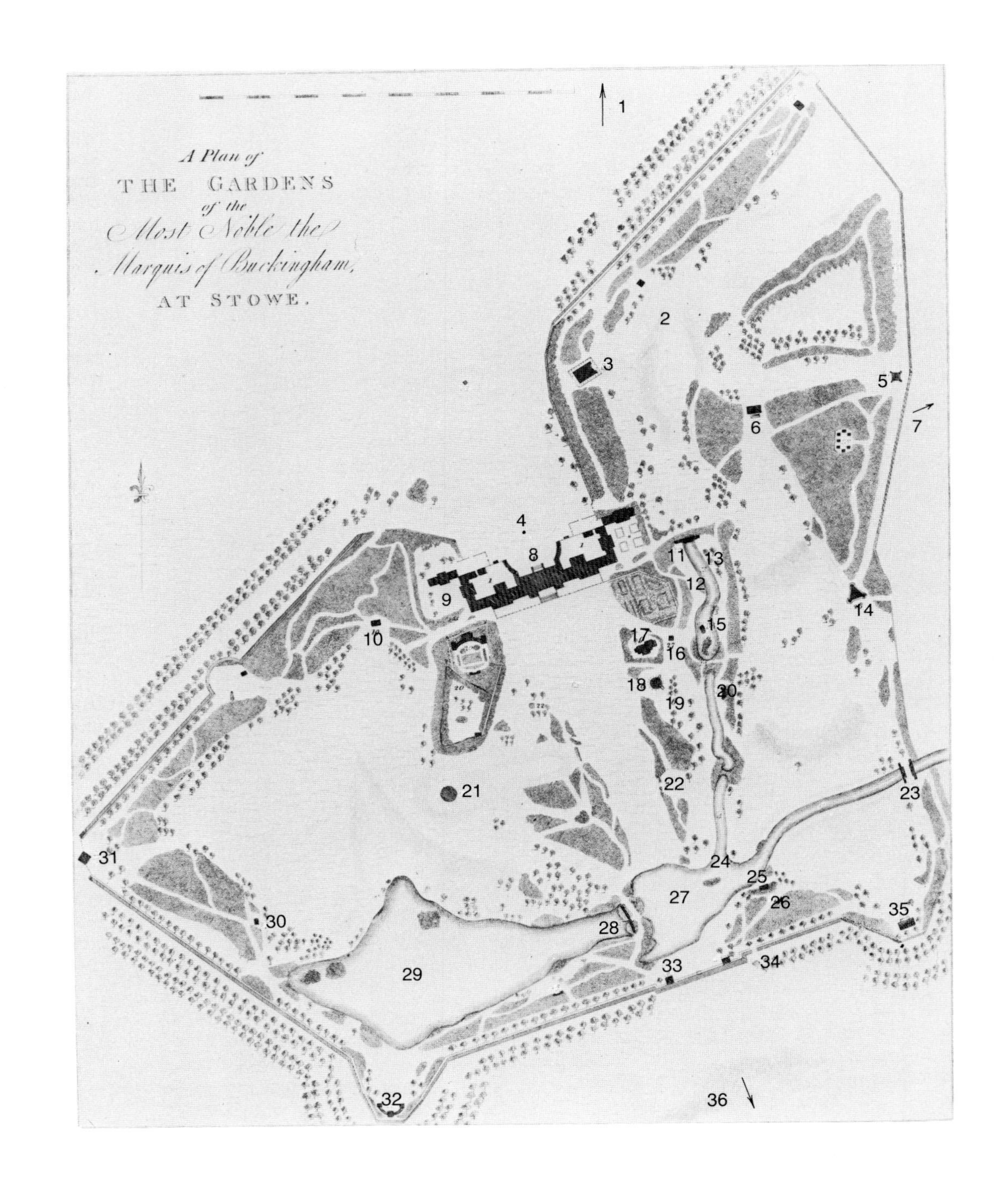

In 1809 Nattes made a copy of the map in the current Stowe guide book, probably to accompany his projected set of engravings. The map printed here is the same one which he copied, but the features have been renumbered and a few of the details slightly altered to indicate more clearly where he took his views.

Note on the Catalogue

All the inscriptions, except where otherwise stated in the catalogue, are written on the mounts of the drawings, with the artist's signature or name and the date at the bottom left, and the title at the bottom centre. All are in ink and in the artist's hand, except for those in capitals, which are in pencil and the hand unidentifiable. In the catalogue the inscriptions are printed in italics. Where a drawing has no inscribed title, its subject is printed in roman type. Measurements are in millimetres, the height before width.

Volume One

1 *OLD BRIDGE AND PART OF THE TOWN OF BUCKINGHAM. I.C. NATTES. DEL. 1809.*

Sepia and grey washes over pencil, with brush in black ink, on wove paper; watermark on mount P. 242 × 358. Plate 1.

2 Buckingham Church from across the river. *I.C. NATTES DEL. 1809.*

Sepia and grey washes over pencil, with brush in black ink, heightened with pen and black ink, on laid paper; watermark crowned fleur-de-lys with GR below; watermark on mount H. 228 × 362.

3 *LODGES, BUCKINGHAM CHURCH &c. I.C. NATTES DEL. 1809.*

Sepia and grey washes over pencil, with brush in black ink, heightened with pen and black ink, and some scratching out, on wove paper; watermark on mount P. 220 × 365. This view is from the north. Plate 2.

4 *LODGES, STOWE. I.C. NATTES DEL. 1809.*

Sepia and grey washes over pencil, with brush in black ink, heightened with pen and black ink, on wove paper. 221 × 366. This view is from the south.

5 *Stowe. The Corinthian Arch, with part of the Gravel path to Buckingham, made in 1806. C. Nattes delt. 1807.*

Grey washes over pencil, with brush in black ink, on laid paper. 224 × 355.

6 *Stowe. View of the Corinthian Arch & the two Columns from the Buckingham road. J.C. Nattes delt. 1805.*

Pencil and grey washes, with brush in black ink, on wove paper; perforations along bottom and right side. 296 × 404. Plate 3.

7 *Stowe. View of the Corinthian Arch. J.C. Nattes delt. 1805.*

Grey washes over pencil, with brush in black ink, on wove paper. 404 × 573. Inscribed in pencil 7 on mount bottom right. Plate 4.

8 *BACK OF THE NEW INN. I.C. NATTES DEL 1809.*

Pencil, black chalk and grey washes, heightened with pen and black ink, on laid paper. 234 × 360.

9 *Stowe. Distant view of the House, from the road to the New Inn. J.C. Nattes delt. 1805.*

Sepia and grey washes over pencil, with brush in black ink, on wove paper. 339 × 526. This is a pleasant fantasy as there can never have been such a view of the house from this point. Plate 5.

10 *Stowe Entrance to the Gardens by the Bell Gate, Back of the Pavillion &c. J.C. Nattes delt. 1805.*

Grey washes over pencil, with brush in black ink, heightened with pen and black ink, on wove paper. 280 × 387. Plate 6.

11 *Stowe. View of the Bell-Gate, & one of the Pavilions. J.C. Nattes delt. 1805.*

Black chalk over pencil, with brush in black ink, and some pen and black ink, on wove paper; watermark J. Whatman. 287 × 386. Inscribed in pencil *NI* top right and *6* top left.

12 *Stowe. View from the Bell-gate Entrance of the Gardens. J.C. Nattes delt. 1805.*

Black chalk and grey wash, with some brush in black ink, and pen and black ink, on wove paper; watermark J. Whatman 1801. 379 × 273. Inscribed in pencil *8* top left.

13 *Stowe A Pavilion. J.C. Nattes delt. 1805.*

Grey washes over pencil, with brush in black ink, heightened with pen and black ink, on laid paper; watermark W. Turner 1803. 369 × 241. Inscribed in pencil *Pavillion* on back. This is the West Lake Pavilion. Plate 32.

14 *Stow The Temple of Venus. C. Nattes delt. 1805.*

Grey washes, with brush in black ink, heightened with pen and black ink, on wove paper. 280 × 382. Inscribed in pencil *4* top right. Plate 7.

15 *Stowe. The Temple of Pastoral Poetry. C. Nattes delt. 1807.*

Grey washes over pencil, with brush in black ink, and some pen and black ink, on laid paper; watermark crowned fleur-de-lys with GR below. 221 × 364.

16 *Stow. The Temple of Venus as seen from the side Arch. C. Nattes delt. 1805.*

Sepia and grey washes over pencil, with brush in black ink, heightened with pen and black ink, on laid paper; watermark A. Blackwell & G. Jones 1801, and crowned fleur-de-lys above monogram AB. 377 × 276. Plate 8.

17 *Stow. From the Interior of the Temple of Venus. C. Nattes delt. 1805.*

Grey washes over pencil, with some brush in black ink, heightened with pen and black ink, on laid paper; watermark crowned fleur-de-lys. 171 × 125.

18 *Stowe. View from the back of the Temple of Venus. C. Nattes delt. 1807.*

Grey washes over pencil, with some brush in black ink, on laid paper; watermark Blackwell & Jones 1801, and crowned fleur-de-lys with monogram AB below. 282 × 383.

19 *Stowe. View of the Gardens, from near the Temple of Venus. C. Nattes delt. 1807.*

Grey washes over pencil, with brush in black ink, and some scratching out, on laid paper; watermark Turner 1803, and crowned fleur-de-lys with WJ below. 283 × 384. Inscribed in pencil *14* top left.

20 *Stowe. View of the Lake, & the Rotunda from near the Temple of Venus. J.C. Nattes delt. 1805.*

Grey washes over pencil, with brush in black ink, on laid paper; watermark W. Turner 1803. 244 × 371.

21 *ROTUNDA FROM OPPOSITE THE TEMPLE OF VENUS, STOWE. I.C. NATTE DEL. 1809.*

Sepia and grey washes over pencil, with brush in black ink, on laid paper; watermark A. Blackwell & G. Jones 1801; watermark on mount H. 276 × 376. Plate 10.

22 *Stowe. The Ruin &c. C. Nattes delt. 1807.*

Grey washes over pencil, with brush in black ink, on laid paper; watermark A. Blackwell & G. Jones 1801, and crowned fleur-de-lys with monogram AB below. 285 × 394. This view is taken looking up the Eleven-Acre Lake towards the Cascade.

23 *Stowe. View from the Head of the Lake. J.C. Nattes delt. 1805.*

Black chalk over pencil, with some brush in black ink, on laid paper; watermark crowned fleur-de-lys with WJ below. 240 × 371. This view is taken looking up the Eleven-Acre Lake towards the Cascade.

24 *Stow The interior of the Lodge, looking towards the Temple of Venus. C. Nattes delt. 1805.*

Black chalk over pencil, with some brush in black ink, heightened with pen and black ink, on laid paper; watermark A. Blackwell & G. Jones 1801, and crowned fleur-de-lys with monogram AB below. 380 × 277. This view is taken from inside the East Boycott Pavilion.

25 *Stow. Boycott Buildings, looking towards the Gothic bridge, lodge &c. C. Nattes. delt. 1805.*

Grey washes over pencil, with some brush in black ink, heightened with pen and black ink, on laid paper; watermark A. Blackwell & G. Jones 1801, and crowned fleur-de-lys with monogram AB below. 387 × 289. Inscribed in pencil *Boycott building* on back. This view is taken from inside the East Boycott Pavilion.

26 *Stowe. The inside of the Boycot Building looking towards the House. J.C. Nattes delt. 1805.*

Grey washes over pencil, with some brush in black ink, heightened with pen and black ink, on laid paper; watermark A. Blackwell & G. Jones 1801, and crowned fleur-de-lys with monogram AB below. 382 × 287. This view is taken from inside the East Boycott Pavilion.

27 *TEMPLE OF BACCHUS, STOWE. I.C. NATTES DEL. 1809.*

Black chalk over pencil, on laid paper; watermark crowned fleur-de-lys with GR below; watermark on mount P. 230 × 363. Plate 11.

28 *INTERIOR OF THE TEMPLE OF BACCHUS. I.C. NATTES. DEL. 1809.*

Grey washes over pencil, heightened with pen and black ink, on wove paper; watermark J. Whatman. 214 × 309.

29 *Stow. The Temple of Venus &c.&c. as seen from the Temple of Bacchus. Drawn by C. Nattes. 19th Augt. 1805.*

Black chalk over pencil, with some brush in black ink, on wove paper; perforations along right side. 274 × 393.

30 *SCHOOL & OFFICES, STOWE. I.C. NATTES. DEL. 1809.*

Sepia and grey washes over pencil, with brush in black ink, heightened with pen and black ink, and some scratching out, on laid paper; watermark L. Munn 1794. 229 × 362.

31 *GREEN-HOUSE &c STOWE. J.C. Nattes. del. 1809.*

Sepia and grey washes over pencil, with brush in black ink, heightened with pen and black ink, and some scratching out, on laid paper; watermark crowned fleur-de-lys with GR below; watermark on mount P. 228 × 361. Inscribed in ink on mount *Green House, Stowe* bottom right, in pencil *Garden* bottom centre. Plate 12.

32 *FROM UNDER THE PORTICO OF THE TEMPLE OF PEACE WITH LORD COBHAMS PILLAR. I.C. NATTES DEL. 1809.*

Sepia and grey washes and pencil, on wove paper. 237 × 343. There never was a Temple of Peace; this drawing depicts the Temple of Concord and Victory.

33 *INTERIOR OF THE TEMPLE OF PEACE, STOWE. I.C. NATTES DEL. 1809.*

Sepia and grey washes over pencil, heightened with pen and black ink, and some scratching out, on wove paper; watermark on mount b. 239 × 365. Inscribed in pencil *73* top left. There never was a Temple of Peace; this drawing depicts the Temple of Concord and Victory.

34 *Stowe. View of Genl Wolfe's Monument, taken from the Temple of Concord & Victory. J.C. Nattes delt. 1805.*

Grey washes, with brush in black ink, heightened with pen and black ink, on laid paper; watermark A. Blackwell & G. Jones 1801, and crowned fleur-de-lys with monogram AB below. 277 × 376. Inscribed in pencil *73* top left; outline in pencil of Wolfe's column to different scale on back. Plate 13.

35 *Stow. Lord Cobham's Pillar. C. Nattes delt. 1805.*

Sepia and grey washes over pencil, with some brush in black ink, on wove paper; perforations along right side. 284 × 402.

36 *Stowe. The Gothick Temple· & Queen's Temple. J.C. Nattes delt. 1805.*

Grey washes over pencil, with brush in black ink, on wove paper. 319 × 472. Plate 14.

37 Lord Cobham's Pillar from the tower of the Gothic Temple.

Grey washes over pencil, with some brush in black ink, heightened with pen and black ink, on laid paper; watermark L. Munn 1794. 163 × 171. Plate 15.

38 *Stowe. View from the Gothick, of the Temple of Friendship, Wooden Bridge &c. J.C. Nattes delt. 1805.*

Black chalk over pencil, with some brush in black ink, on laid paper; watermark A. Blackwell & G. Jones 1801, and crowned fleur-de-lys with monogram AB below. 279 × 380. Inscribed in pencil *from the red Building* on back.

39 *Stowe Entrance to the Palladian Bridge, Temple of Friendship &c. C. Nattes. delt. 1805.*

Grey washes over pencil, with brush in black ink, heightened with pen and black ink, on laid paper; watermark Turner 1803, and crowned fleur-de-lys. 277 × 376.

40 *Stow The Palladian Bridge. C. Nattes delt. 1805.*

Black chalk over pencil, with some pen and black ink, on laid paper; watermark Turner 1803, and crowned fleur-de-lys with WJ below. 284 ×374. Plate 16.

41 *Stow. The Temple of Friendship. C. Nattes delt. 1805.*

Black chalk over pencil, with some pen and black ink, on laid paper; watermark A. Blackwell & G. Jones 1801, and crowned fleur-de-lys with monogram AB below. 285 × 391. Plate 17.

42 *Stow Interior of the Side Arch of the Temple of Friendship. C. Nattes delt.*

Grey washes over pencil, heightened with pen and black ink, on wove paper. 401 × 253.

43 *Stowe. View of the Gothick Temple, taken near the Temple of Friendship. J.C. Nattes. delt. 1805.*

Grey washes over pencil, with brush in black ink, and some pen and black ink, on laid paper; watermark A. Blackwell & G. Jones 1801, and crowned fleur-de-lys with monogram AB below. 277 × 378. Inscribed in pencil *25* top right.

44 *Stowe. View of the Queen's Temple. J.C. Nattes delt. 1805.*

Black chalk and grey wash, with brush in black ink, on laid paper; watermark A. Blackwell & G. Jones 1801, and crowned fleur-de-lys with monogram AB below. 281 × 394. Inscribed in pencil *48* top right and *48* on back.

45 *Stowe. View of the Cascade & Lake. J.C. Nattes delt. 1805.*

Grey washes over pencil, with brush in black ink, on wove paper. 295 × 415. Plate 18.

46 *Stowe View from the Cascade. C. Nattes delt. 1807.*

Grey washes over pencil, with brush in black ink, and some pen and black ink, on laid paper; watermark A. Blackwell & G. Jones 1801, and crowned fleur-de-lys with monogram AB below. 287 × 407. This view is over the Eleven-Acre Lake.

47 *Stowe. View of the Lake, from the Top of the Cascade. J.C. Nattes delt. 1805.*

Black chalk over pencil, with some brush in black ink, on laid paper; watermark crowned fleur-de-lys. 238 × 369. Inscribed in pencil *Top of the Cascade* on back. This view is over the Eleven-Acre Lake.

48 *Stowe. View of the Octagon Water from the Cascade. J.C. Nattes delt. 1805.*

Grey washes over pencil, with brush in black ink, on wove paper. 273 × 374. Plate 19.

49 *Stowe. View of the Octagon Water taken from the walk leading to the House from the Bell-gate. J.C. Nattes delt. 1805.*

Grey washes over pencil, with brush in black ink, and pen and black ink, on laid paper; watermark W. Turner 1803. 240 × 369.

50 *Stowe. The Octagon Water. J.C. Nattes delt. 1805.*

Grey washes, with brush in black ink, heightened with pen and black ink, and some scratching out, on laid paper; watermark crowned fleur-de-lys with monogram AB below. 242 × 374.

51 *Stowe View of the Wooden & Palladian bridges. J.C. Nattes delt. 1805.*

Black chalk over pencil, with brush in black ink, and some pen and black ink, on laid paper; watermark A. Blackwell & G. Jones 1801, and crowned fleur-de-lys with monogram AB below. 278 × 379.

52 *Stow The rustic Seat. &c. C. Nattes delt. 1805.*

Black chalk over pencil, with some pen and black ink, on laid paper; watermark A. Blackwell & G. Jones 1801. 232 × 366. The Pebble Alcove is in the left foreground.

Volume Two

53 *Stowe. View of the Rotunda, & Queen Caroline's Monument. J.C. Nattes delt. 1805.*

Grey washes over pencil, with brush in black ink, and pen and black ink, on laid paper. 278 × 386. Plate 20.

54 *ROTUNDA &c, STOWE. I.C. NATTES DEL. 1809.*

Black chalk over pencil, on laid paper; watermark A. Blackwell & G. Jones 1801, and crowned fleur-de-lys with monogram AB below. 275 × 377.

55 *Stowe. A distant view of the South front of the House & King William's Column. J.C. Nattes delt. 1805.*

Grey washes over pencil, with brush in black ink, on laid paper; watermark Blackwell & Jones 1801, and crowned fleur-de-lys with monogram AB below. 278 × 396. The statue represents George II, not William III.

56 *Stowe. The Rotunda, from the walk leading to Queen Caroline's Monument. J.C. Nattes delt. 1805.*

Black chalk over pencil, with pen and black ink, on laid paper; watermark crowned fleur-de-lys. 239 × 369.

57 *Stowe. View of Queen Caroline's Monument. J.C. Nattes delt. 1805.*

Grey washes over pencil, with brush in black ink, heightened with pen and black ink, on laid paper; watermark W. Turner 1803. 333 × 241. Plate 43.

58 *Stowe. View of Queen Caroline's Monument & the Rotunda. J.C. Nattes delt. 1805.*

Black chalk over pencil, with some brush in black ink, heightened with pen and black ink, on laid paper; watermark Turner 1803, and crowned fleur-de-lys with WJ below; perforations along top and right side. 296 × 390.

59 *Stowe Grecian valley from the New grotto. J.C. Nattes delt. 1805.*

Grey washes over pencil, with some brush in black ink, and pen and black ink, and some scratching out, on laid paper; watermark A. Blackwell & G. Jones 1801, and crowned fleur-de-lys with monogram AB below. 276 × 374. Inscribed in pencil on mount *Ice House* bottom centre. 'The New Grotto' is in fact the old grotto, which had been extensively altered. Plate 21.

60 *Stow. The Group of Hercules & Anteus &c. Grecian valley. C. Nattes delt. 1805.*

Black chalk and grey wash over pencil, with some pen and black ink, on laid paper; watermark A. Blackwell & G. Jones 1801, and crowned fleur-de-lys with monogram AB below. 276 × 385.

61 *Stowe. View of the Queen's Temple. J.C. Nattes delt. 1805.*

Sepia and grey washes over pencil, with brush in black ink, heightened with pen and black ink, on wove paper. 254 × 379. Plate 22.

62 *Stowe. View of the Back from of (sic) the Queen's Temple & Lord Cobham's Pillar. J.C. Nattes delt. 1805.*

Grey washes over pencil, with brush in black ink, on wove paper. 284 × 416. Plate 23.

63 *INTERIOR OF THE LADIES TEMPLE LOOKING TOWARDS THE PARK. I.C. NATTE DEL 1809.*

Sepia and grey washes over pencil, on wove paper; watermark J. Whatman; watermark on mount H. 227 × 324.

64 *INTERIOR OF THE LADIES TEMPLE, THE TEMPLE OF FRIENDSHIP AND THE TRIUMPHAL ARCH. I.C. NATTES DEL 1809.*

Sepia and grey washes over pencil, on wove paper; watermark on mount P. 253 × 422. Plate 24.

65 *Stow The Grotto. C. Nattes delt. 1805.*

Black chalk over pencil, with brush in black ink, and pen and black ink, on laid paper; watermark A. Blackwell & G. Jones 1801, and crowned fleur-de-lys with monogram AB below. 280 × 378. Plate 25.

66 *Stow Inside of the Grotto, with temporary Obelisk and Bridge. &c. C. Nattes det. 1805.*

Black chalk over pencil, with some pen and black ink, on laid paper; watermark A. Blackwell & G. Jones 1801, and crowned fleur-de-lys with monogram AB below. 279 × 381.

67 *Stowe. View of the Water below the Grotto, & the Temporary bridge & Seats erected at the Fête given to the Prince of Wales in 1805. J.C. Nattes delt. 1805.*

Grey washes over pencil, with brush in black ink, and some pen and black ink, and some scratching out, on wove paper. 282 × 386. Inscribed in pencil *68* top right.

68 *Stowe. View of Capn. Cooke's Monument & the water below the Grotto. J.C. Nattes delt. 1805.*

Black chalk, with some brush in black ink, and some pen and black ink, on wove paper; watermark J. Whatman. 284 × 453.

69 *Stowe. View of the water below the Grotto & the temporary Bridge & Obelisk, erected & Illuminated at the Fête given to the Prince of Wales 1805. J.C. Nattes delt. 1805.*

Grey washes over pencil, with brush in black ink, and pen and black ink, on laid paper; watermark A. Blackwell & G. Jones 1801, and crowned fleur-de-lys with monogram AB below; perforations along top and right side. 277 × 391. Inscribed in pencil *67* top right; inscribed in pencil *temporary bridge & Obelisk* on back. Plate 26.

70 *Stowe. View of the Grotto & Fountain. J.C. Nattes delt. 1805.*

Grey washes over pencil, with brush in black ink, and pen and black ink, on wove paper. 290 × 394. Plate 27.

71 *Stowe. View of Capn. Cooke, & Capn. Grenville's monument taken from the fountain. J.C. Nattes delt. 1805.*

Grey washes over pencil, with brush in black ink, and pen and black ink, and some scratching out, on wove paper. 288 × 423. Plate 28.

72 *Stowe. View of the Temple of the Worthies. J.C. Nattes delt. 1805.*

Grey washes over pencil, with brush in black ink, heightened with pen and black ink, on laid paper; watermark A. Blackwell & G. Jones 1801, and crowned fleur-de-lys with monogram AB below. 278 × 381. Plate 29.

73 *Stowe. View of the Temple of the Worthies. J.C. Nattes delt. 1805.*

Grey washes over pencil, with brush in black ink, on wove paper. 282 × 386. Inscribed in pencil *38* top left. Plate 30.

74 *REMAINS OF A TEMPLE AT STOWE. I.C. NATTES DEL. 1809.*

Grey washes over pencil, with brush in black ink, and pen and black ink, on laid paper; watermark crowned fleur-de-lys with GR below. 230 × 363. The identity of this building is not clear. It may be the Temple of Modern Virtue, which was intentionally built as a ruin.

75 *Stowe. View of the Naval Column, erected in Memory of Capn. Grenville; & distant of the South Portico. J.C. Nattes delt. 1805.*

Sepia and grey washes over pencil, with brush in black ink, heightened with pen and black ink, on laid paper. 287 × 255.

76 *Stow. The Temple of Antient Virtue. C. Nattes. delt. 1805.*

Black chalk over pencil, with brush in black ink, and pen and black ink, on laid paper; perforations along top. 286 × 259. Plate 31.

77 *Stow View from the interior of the Temple of Antient Virtue. C. Nattes delt. 1805.*

Black chalk over pencil, with brush in black ink, heightened with pen and black ink, on laid paper. 279 × 162. Plate 9.

78 *Stow Church. Drawn by C. Nattes.*

Black chalk over pencil, on laid paper; watermark A. Blackwell & G. Jones 1801, and crowned fleur-de-lys with monogram AB below; perforations along top. 293 × 403. Plate 33.

79 *DORIC ARCH, PALLADIAN BRIDGE AND CASTLE AT STOWE. I.C. NATTES DEL. 1809.*

Sepia and grey washes over pencil, with brush in black ink, and some scratching out, on wove paper. 240 × 370. Plate 34.

80 *BRIDGE, ISLAND, AND PAVILLION, STOWE. I.C. NATTES DEL. 1809.*

Black chalk over pencil, on laid paper; watermark A. Blackwell & G. Jones 1801, and crowned fleur-de-lys with monogram AB below; watermark on mount L. 275 × 377.

81 *Stowe View of the Gardens, Bridge & one of the Pavilions. C. Nattes delt. 1807.*

Grey washes over pencil, with brush in black ink, and pen and black ink, on laid paper; watermark A. Blackwell & G. Jones 1801, and crowned fleur-de-lys with monogram AB below. 277 × 378. Plate 35.

82 *Stowe. View of the Wooden bridge, the Pavilion & the Octagon water, taken from the banks opposite to Congreve's Monument. J.C. Nattes delt. 1805.*

Grey washes over pencil, with brush in black ink, and some pen and black ink, on laid paper; watermark A. Blackwell & G. Jones 1801, and crowned fleur-de-lys with monogram AB below; perforations along left side. 280 × 402. Plate 36.

83 *Stowe. View of the Island & one of the Pavilions. C. Nattes delt. 1807.*

Grey washes over pencil, with brush in black ink, and some scratching out, on laid paper; watermark W. J. Turner 1803, and crowned fleur-de-lys with WJ below. 274 × 387.

84 *Stowe. View of the Shell grotto & Palladian Bridge &c. J.C. Nattes delt. 1805.*

Black chalk over pencil, with brush in black ink, and pen and black ink, on laid paper; watermark Blackwell & Jones 1801, and crowned fleur-de-lys with monogram AB below. 278 × 381. Plate 37.

85 *Stowe View of Congreve's Monument, & Pavilion. J.C. Nattes delt. 1805.*

Black chalk over pencil, with some brush in black ink, heightened with pen and black ink, and some scratching out, on laid paper; watermark crowned fleur-de-lys with monogram AB below. 286 × 230. Plate 38.

86 *Stowe. The Lodges at the Entrance from the London road. J.C. Nattes delt. 1805.*

Grey washes over pencil, with brush in black ink, on laid paper; watermark A. Blackwell & G. Jones 1801, and crowned fleur-de-lys with monogram AB below. 287 × 395. Inscribed in pencil *28* top right. Plate 40.

87 *Stowe. The Bridge & Entrance Lodges. J.C. Nattes delt. 1805.*

Grey washes, with brush in black ink, heightened with pen and black ink, on laid paper; watermark A. Blackwell & G. Jones 1801, and crowned fleur-de-lys with monogram AB below; perforations along left side. 262 × 397. Plate 41.

88 *Stow Obelisk to the Memory of General Wolf. C. Nattes delt. 1805.*

Pencil, on laid paper; watermark Blackwell & G. Jones 1801, and fleur-de-lys with monogram AB below. 390 × 291. Inscribed in pencil *68 steps; 2 foot high gave 2 . . . shadow; 34* on back. Plate 42.

89 *Stowe. View of the round Tower in the Park. J.C. Nattes delt. 1805.*

Grey washes over pencil, with brush in black ink, heightened with pen and black ink, and some scratching out, on laid paper; watermark Blackwell & Jones 1801, and crowned fleur-de-lys with monogram AB below. 278 × 372. This was built as a keeper's lodge. A few years later it was renamed the Bourbon Tower and converted for use by the militia. Plate 44.

90 Equestrian Statue of George I.

Pencil, heightened with pen and black ink, on wove paper; watermark J. Whatman. 349 × 261. Inscribed in ink *Equestrian Statue of George I in the Park;* altered to *II* in pencil; and in pencil *STOWE 1805.* Reproduced on page 5.

91 *Stowe View of part of the Back front of the House. J.C. Nattes delt. 1805.*

Grey washes over pencil, with brush in black ink, heightened with pen and black ink, on wove paper; watermark J. Whatman. 306 × 464. Plate 45.

92 *Stowe. View taken from the Portico of the North front of the House. J.C. Nattes delt. 1805.*

Grey washes over pencil, with some brush in black ink, on wove paper; watermark J. Whatman. 282 × 383. Plate 46.

93 *Stowe. View taken from the Portico of the North front of the House. J.C. Nattes delt. 1805.*

Grey washes over pencil, with some brush in black ink, on wove paper. 280 × 380.

94 The Marble Saloon.

Grey wash over pencil, with pen and black ink, on heavy wove paper. 259 × 387. This is by an unknown amateur hand. Other versions of this drawing are in the Morgan-Grenville Collection and in Stowe School Library.

95 *Stowe. View taken within the Portico of the South front of the House. J.C. Nattes delt. 1805.*

Grey washes over pencil, with some brush in black ink, on wove paper; watermark J. Whatman. 284 × 401.

96 *Stowe. View taken within the Portico of the South front of the House. J.C. Nattes delt. 1805.*

Grey washes over pencil, with some brush in black ink, on wove paper. 266 × 393. Plate 47.

97 *Stowe. View taken from the Entrance under the North Portico. J.C. Nattes delt, 1805.*

Grey washes over pencil, heightened with pen and black ink, on laid paper; watermark crowned fleur-de-lys with monogram AB below. 305 × 243. Plate 39.

98 *Stowe. Interior view of the Egyptian Hall. J.C. Nattes delt. 1805.*

Grey washes over pencil, with some brush in black ink, on wove paper. 198 × 275. Plate 48.

99 Basement Cellars to the House.

Grey washes over pencil, with some brush in black ink, heightened with pen and black ink, on wove paper; watermark L. Munn 1794. 184 × 301.

100 *Stowe. The Bath. C. Nattes delt. 1807.*

Grey washes over pencil, with some brush in black ink, on laid paper; watermark L. Munn 1794. 133 × 198. This bath still exists, but is boarded over. Plate 49.

101 *Stowe The Passage leading to the Gothic Room. C. Nattes delt. 1807.*

Grey washes over pencil, heightened with pen and black ink, on laid paper; watermark crowned fleur-de-lys with GR below. 212 × 228. Plate 50.

102 The Stable Court, now known as Cobham Court.

Grey washes over pencil, with brush in black ink, and pen and black ink, and some scratching out, on laid paper; watermark L. Munn 1794. 238 × 364. Plate 51.

103 *The Aviary* (inscribed in pencil at a later date).

Grey washes, with brush in black ink, and some pen and black ink, and some scratching out, on laid paper; watermark crowned fleur-de-lys with GR below. 241 × 367.

104 *OFFICES &c STOWE. J.C. Nattes del 1809.*

Grey washes over pencil, with brush in black ink, heightened with pen and black ink, and some scratching out, on laid paper; watermark L. Munn 1794; watermark on mount P. 229 × 361.

105 *KITCHEN &c. STOWE. I.C. NATTES. DEL. 1809.*

Sepia and grey washes over pencil, with brush in black ink, and some pen and black ink, and some scratching out, on laid paper; watermark crowned fleur-de-lys with GR below. 229 × 361. Inscriptions in pencil which are only partially legible *To morrow from . . . walk to the City take the . . . and have an afternoon . . . with . . .* on back; in different hand *. . . Port Royall . . . sur les . . . Science par le . . .* The kitchens were on the west side. This shows part of the east service court on the way to the stables and the coach yard.

Plates

The Old Bridge and Town of Buckingham *Cat. No. 1*

The Avenue Lodges and Buckingham Church *Cat. No. 3*

The Corinthian Arch *Cat. No. 6*

Plate 4

The Corinthian Arch *Cat. No. 7*

A Distant View of the House *Cat. No. 9*

The Bell Gate *Cat. No. 10*

The Temple of Venus *Cat. No. 14*

Plate 8

The Temple of Venus *Cat. No. 16*

Plate 9

The Grenville Column from the Temple of Ancient Virtue *Cat. No. 77*

The Eleven-Acre Lake and the Rotunda *Cat. No. 21*

The Temple of Bacchus *Cat. No. 27*

The Orangery *Cat. No. 31*

View towards Wolfe's Obelisk *Cat. No. 34*

The Gothic Temple *Cat. No. 36*

View of Lord Cobham's Pillar from the Tower of the Gothic Temple *Cat. No. 37*

The Palladian Bridge *Cat. No. 40*

The Temple of Friendship *Cat. No. 41*

The Eleven-Acre Lake and the Cascade *Cat. No. 45*

The Octagon Lake and the Palladian Bridge *Cat. No. 48*

The Rotunda and Queen Caroline's Monument *Cat. No. 53*

The Grecian Valley *Cat. No. 59*

The Queen's Temple *Cat. No. 61*

The Queen's Temple and Lord Cobham's Pillar *Cat. No. 62*

The Temple of Friendship from the Queen's Temple *Cat. No. 64*

The Grotto *Cat. No. 65*

View of the Alder River below the Grotto *Cat. No. 69*

The Seasons' Fountain and the Grotto *Cat. No. 70*

Captain Cook's Monument and the Grenville Column *Cat. No. 71*

The Temple of British Worthies *Cat. No. 72*

The Temple of British Worthies *Cat. No. 73*

Plate 31

The Temple of Ancient Virtue *Cat. No. 76*

Plate 32

The West Lake Pavilion *Cat. No. 13*

Stowe Church *Cat. No. 78*

View through the Doric Arch *Cat. No. 79*

The Wooden Bridge and Lake Pavilion *Cat. No. 81*

The Wooden Bridge and the Octagon Lake *Cat. No. 82*

The Pebble Alcove and the Palladian Bridge *Cat. No. 84*

Plate 38

The Congreve Monument *Cat. No. 85*

Plate 39

View from the Carriage Entrance under the North Portico *Cat. No. 97*

The Oxford Gate and Lodge *Cat. No. 86*

The Oxford Bridge and Oxford Gate *Cat. No. 87*

Wolfe's Obelisk *Cat. No. 88*

Queen Caroline's Monument *Cat. No. 57*

The Keeper's Lodge *Cat. No. 89*

The North Front *Cat. No. 91*

View from the North Portico *Cat. No. 92*

The South Portico *Cat. No. 96*

The Egyptian Entry *Cat. No. 98*

The Bath *Cat. No. 100*

View along the Basement Passage towards the Gothic Library *Cat. No. 101*

The Stable Court *Cat. No. 102*

Printed in England by: White Bros. (Printers) Ltd., 21-25 South Lambeth Road, London, SW8 1TH 01-582 1282